A New ... for the Lodge

Written by Ben Smith
Illustrated by Peter Campbell

Bertie and Betty Beaver were very busy beavers. They used to live a long way up the river, but Bertie and Betty moved down the river to where the water didn't flow so fast. They built a new dam and a new lodge near a road that led to a little cabin. They liked living there.

Bertie and Betty liked their new lodge. They told their friends how nice it was. So lots of their friends moved to live near them. Bertie and Betty helped their friends build new dams and lodges to live in.

Tommy and Tammy Tramper lived in the big city, but they also had a little cabin in the woods, near a river. Tommy and Tammy were going to their cabin for two weeks. Tommy and Tammy were going to hike in the hills. They liked hiking.

As Tammy and Tommy drove down the road to their cabin, Tammy called out "Oh no! Look! The road is flooded!"

"How can the road be flooded?" asked Tommy. "It hasn't been raining. Let's have a look."

"There," said Tammy. "It's a beaver lodge. We'll have to break it down."

So Tommy and Tammy got to work and broke down Betty and Bertie's new lodge.

When Bertie and Betty heard the sound of the car, they swam away. They went back to where they used to live. They went to see some of their friends.

"We'll be safe here," said Bertie to Betty. "We'll go back to our lodge later."

Later that night, Bertie and Betty went home.

"Where has our lodge gone?" said Betty.

"Look!" said Bertie. "Someone has broken it down. We'll just have to build it again."

So Bertie and Betty called all their friends to come and help them. The beavers worked very hard. It took them all night to build another new lodge for Bertie and Betty.

In the morning, Tommy and Tammy got up early. They were going hiking in the hills.

"Oh no!" yelled Tammy. "The road is flooded!"

"But it didn't rain last night," said Tommy. "How can the road be flooded?"

Tommy went to look, and he saw a big pile of trunks and branches.

"It's those beavers again," he called to Tammy. "We'll just have to break down their lodge all over again. Then the road won't flood."

That night, Betty and Bertie rebuilt their lodge. And so it went on for five more days. Every day, Tommy and Tammy found the road flooded and they broke down the beavers' lodge. And every night, Betty and Bertie and their friends worked hard and built their lodge again.

"That's it!" said Tammy to Tommy one morning. "I have a plan. Beavers are awake at night. We'll put a lantern right where they have been building their lodge. The beavers will think it's daytime and they won't build there again."

"I think that might work," said Tommy.

So Tommy and Tammy got a big lantern. They put the big lantern right where the beavers kept on building their new lodge.

That night, when Betty and Bertie swam back home, they got a real surprise.

"What's this?" asked Bertie.

"Whoever is breaking down our lodge must have left a light for us," said Betty. "Maybe it'll hold the trunks and branches in place. Why don't we build our new lodge around it? Come on, let's start now."

So that night, Bertie and Betty and their friends built another new lodge for Bertie and Betty. But this time, the beavers built their lodge right around Tammy and Tommy's lantern.

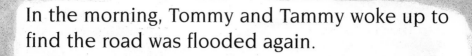

In the morning, Tommy and Tammy woke up to find the road was flooded again.

"Oh no!" said Tommy and Tammy, as they stood looking at the flooded road. "It looks like the beavers have used the lantern we put there as a light for their new lodge!"